Chocolate
MAGIC

If you enjoy reading this book, you might like to try another story from the

MAMMOTH READ

series:

Chocolate
MAGiC

previously published as The Chocolate Touch II

Patrick Skene Catling

Illustrated by **Philip Hopman**

mammoth

First published in Great Britain 1997 by Mammoth
as *The Chocolate Touch II*
Reissued in this edition 2000
by Mammoth, an imprint of Egmont Children's Books Limited
239 Kensington High Street, London W8 6SA

ISBN 0 7497 4211 9

10 9 8 7 6 5 4 3 2 1

A CIP catalogue record for this title
is available from the British Library

Printed in Great Britain
by Cox & Wyman Ltd, Reading, Berkshire

Having had the honour of interviewing Mickey Mouse in Walt Disney World on the occasion of his fiftieth birthday, the author wishes to dedicate this story to Mickey's continuing health and happiness in his sixties.

One

SCHOOL WAS OUT! As they ran to the playground, children cheered. Mary Midas and her brother John had been looking forward to this time ever since their father had been promoted to his company's New York office and he promised the family a winter holiday in Florida. Tomorrow they would be on their way.

'Think of it!' Mary said. 'We'll soon be in the Magic Kingdom! Mickey Mouse and Minnie Mouse! Donald Duck and Goofy! I can hardly wait.'

'There's more to Walt Disney World than that,' John replied with a cleverer-than-you smile. 'There's some fabulous high-tech scientific stuff as well. Robots . . . and space things.'

He was less than two years older than Mary. When they were very young two years seemed an enormous difference. But now, in many ways, she was catching up. He often talked as if he knew much more than she did. It was true that he could remember cricket batting averages and the names of England's top-scoring soccer stars. Hooked by video games, he had begun to think of himself as some kind of electronics whizz kid. And now that they were living in America, he knew all the American pop groups in the top ten. But Mary read more books, she painted pictures of animals and flowers, and she had not dropped out of what she called 'real music'. These days, John never took his trumpet out of its case, while Mary still had weekly piano lessons and faithfully did an hour's practice every evening.

Mary was pretty. She had big, blue eyes, and she brushed her yellow hair until it shone. She was neat. She  kept her clothes on hangers and folded in drawers, and she made her bed, without any wrinkles, as soon as she got out of it. And she was really serious about homework. She got almost all of it perfectly correct, and always finished it on time.

John was really casual. Their mother often said his tangled red hair  looked like a bird's nest – the nest of a very sloppy bird. He spent quite a lot of time just sort of fooling around.

If you met them for the first time that December, you probably would have given Mary nine out of ten marks for goodness, and John a lot fewer. But that goes to show that usually you cannot tell everything about someone from first impressions. Mary had a guilty secret.

Try asking this question in your classroom: who likes chocolate? Nearly everybody in the room, including the teacher, will probably raise their hands. Why shouldn't they? There is nothing wrong with liking chocolate. In America the average person eats five kilos of chocolate a year – plain chocolate and milk chocolate; crunchy chocolates, chewy chocolates and creamy chocolates; chocolate Santa Clauses and chocolate Easter eggs and even chocolate rabbits.

Eating chocolate is quite all right if you don't make a pig of yourself. Then it can be an unhealthy habit. Mary, unfortunately, since arriving in New York, had become secretly rather piggish.

She had fallen in love in a big way at her most recent birthday party. Her chocolate

birthday cake had thick chocolate icing and a sweet, smooth chocolate filling between layers. Her mother then served chocolate ice-cream sundaes as a special treat, smothered in thick chocolate syrup.

After that feast, however much chocolate Mary ate, she never felt it was enough. She knew she should not eat so much chocolate – it might make holes in her teeth and spots on her skin – but it was so delicious (especially Strawberry Delights) that she could not help herself.

She enjoyed reading about chocolate. In the reference department of the local public library, the librarian found her a book about the history of chocolate. The book said that cacao trees, whose beans are needed to make chocolate, were grown first in South America. The most famous North American chocolate manufacturer was Milton Hershey, who built his first chocolate factory in 1903. His chocolate bars became so popular that a whole town was named after him – Hershey, Pennsylvania, where the air is sweet with the scent of chocolate.

Reading about chocolate always gave Mary a sharp longing to eat some. Chocolate commercials on television made her drool. She spent most of her pocket money, sometimes all of it, on chocolate.

On a typical Saturday she would smuggle chocolates up to her bedroom, lock the door, and stay until she had eaten every one.

Though she had been a warmly generous sister from earliest girlhood, greed was making her sneaky and mean. She never offered to share any chocolate with her brother.

John was puzzled. He did not know what was going on. Mary seemed to be changing. He felt that something was wrong. Even on the supposedly happy afternoon before their long-awaited trip to Florida, she was unnaturally quiet, as if she had something private on her mind that she did not want him to know about.

'What's the matter?' he asked her. 'Is it something I've done? Something I've said?'

'Nothing's the matter.'

'Well, do you want to go to the park? I've made a new kite. It's a picture of Miss Whipsnade.' Miss Whipsnade was John's favourite new teacher, but he sometimes made fun of her, drawing cartoons that exaggerated the length of her bony nose.

'Why don't you go and fly it?' Mary suggested. 'I'm busy.'

'You're always too busy to play,' he complained. 'What do you do in your room?'

'I have to get ready for tomorrow. Mummy's taking me to the mall. And then I have to pack.'

'Packing only takes five minutes.'

'Maybe the way you pack. It takes me longer.'

She was an expert at annoying him. If that was the way she was going to be, he, too, could be annoying.

'You know what, Mary? Your face is getting really fat!'

Mary flinched as if stung, but did not reply.

Gosh, John thought. She won't play. She won't fight. Isn't she going to do anything to make life interesting at Walt Disney World?

They did not know it yet, but she certainly was.

Two

THE NEW SHOPPING mall was magnificent. Its name was Eldorado, meaning 'the golden place', which is what the Spanish conquerors of America imagined they would find when they arrived there five hundred years ago. The mall was bigger and shinier than anything they could have hoped for.

There were tall white pillars at the entrance. Inside, the high ceilings, the walls and floors were of polished white marble, brilliantly lighted by chandeliers glittering like diamonds. Flowers perfumed the pleasantly cool air, and there was continuous soft music, with a harp and violins.

The rows of bright shops sold almost everything you could think of, and a lot of things you'd probably never thought of before. Mrs Midas and Mary enjoyed walking around for hours, mostly only looking. They didn't buy much but talked a lot about all sorts of possibilities.

'Oh, no! Not the mall!' John would protest with a groan. Mr Midas would mutter something about his computer or cutting the grass. They did not know how to enjoy the idea of shopping, how to appreciate the mall as a wonderful museum, an art gallery, an Aladdin's cave of treasures. They didn't even care about the pastries in the Paris Café. They encouraged mother and daughter to go to the mall on their own, and that suited them fine.

On this occasion, Mary and her mother went first to one of the boutiques that specialised in 'Tropical Vacation Sportswear'.

'We must get nice swimming things,' Mrs Midas said. 'The hotel is sure to have a great pool. People swim every day down there.'

They examined dozens of colourful new designs and finally selected two swimming costumes they agreed on; a red bikini for Mrs Midas and a pale-blue costume for Mary, who was more conservative.

'The blue is exactly the same colour as your eyes,' Mrs Midas said. Mary blushed with modest pleasure.

'We'd better get shorts for the others,' Mrs Midas said. They quickly chose navy blue for Mr Midas and green for John.

'He'll say he hates this,' Mary predicted with a smile.

'No, he won't, darling,' Mrs Midas

assured her. 'John doesn't mind what he wears. Anyway, the green will go well with his auburn hair.'

'Don't tell him that. He'd have a fit.'

They laughed. They thought John's red hair was funny, even when they called it auburn.

'I have to go to the drugstore and one or two other places,' Mrs Midas said. 'Suntan lotion, and I have nothing to wear in the evening. Would you be an angel and pick up a few bits and pieces from the supermarket?'

She gave Mary the list.

Mary took her time at the supermarket, pushing the trolley up and down the long aisles. She knew there was no rush while her mother tried on dresses.

At last, though, Mary decided she should check out. There were lines at all the cash registers except one. At one end of the row sat an old man in a white coat. As all the cashiers were young women, Mary thought the old man was one of the managers. He, too, was sitting at a register, but no customers were checking out that way. When Mary moved towards a line, he gave her a friendly smile, held up a finger and beckoned to her.

'This way, Mary,' he said.

She wondered how he knew her name but she was too shy to ask. His white hair and glasses and pink face and white moustache reminded her of Grandfather Midas, her father's father.

'Special service here,' the man said encouragingly, 'if your name is Mary Midas. It is, isn't it?'

'Yes,' Mary said. 'But . . .?' She couldn't think of what to say. When someone knows your name, you feel you should know theirs. It seems a bit rude not to.

'No waiting for you here,' he said.

'Thank you,' she said, trying not to look puzzled. She unloaded her few purchases on to the counter – not much was needed on the eve of a holiday. The old man accepted her two bills and gave her some small change.

Mary took the carrier bag and thanked him again. She was about to move on when she noticed something odd about one of the coins. It was the size of a quarter. It was the silver-grey of a quarter, but it definitely wasn't a quarter. It did not have the familiar portrait of George Washington on one side and the picture of an eagle on the other. She felt the small hairs on the back of her neck prickle with amazement as she recognised her own face on one side of the coin – her own face but with cheeks that were absolutely round – and, on the other side, the initials M.M.

'Hey!' she exclaimed. 'What's this?'

'Ah!' the old man replied. 'You are right; it is not an ordinary coin. I have given you the right change. The coin is a bonus, specially for you, for which, sooner or later, you are sure to be grateful. It is a coin of a kind minted only for children who are unusually fond of chocolate. In exchange for this coin, if you wish, you can have one of my special chocolate boxes. They are on display back in the far corner on the left. Perhaps you did not notice them the first time around. You can go there now, if you like, and help yourself to one, unless you feel you should first obtain your mother's permission.'

'A box of chocolates, all for me?'

'A chocolate box.'

'I don't have to get anyone's permission,' Mary said. 'I'm sure my mother wouldn't object.'

The old man simply nodded and smiled.

Mary hurried back to where she found a tall stack of gold and purple chocolate boxes, the biggest she had ever seen.

'Wow!' she gasped.

As she grabbed one, her hands trembled and her mouth watered with greedy excitement.

When she took her box back to the checkout, the old man was nowhere to be seen. She did not wait. She put the strange coin on the counter, stuffed the box into her carrier bag, and got out of the supermarket without delay.

She almost told her mother about the surprise gift, but then thought perhaps it would be better not to. When they got home, Mary almost showed it to John, but then she didn't. She hid the box under the clothes in her suitcase.

Something special, she told herself, for me, myself, on my holiday.

It was, in fact, something very special, as the old man had promised, for it would give Mary the magic chocolate touch.

Three

THE JOURNEY WAS easy. The next day, the Midas family flew to Orlando International Airport, drove in a rental car along the Beeline Expressway to Walt Disney World, and rode the monorail from a huge carpark to the newest, most luxurious hotel in the Magic Kingdom.

'Elegant,' Mrs Midas murmured approvingly.

'Super,' Mr Midas agreed. 'We're surrounded by golf courses.'

Mary looked down from a window in their suite.

'Look, John!' she said.

John went and stood beside her. They could see palm-trees and the red and purple blossoms of bougainvillaea around a large, circular swimming-pool with two smaller circles at one end.

'Mickey Mouse!' Mary marvelled. 'Even the pool!'

'They think of everything,' John acknowledged. 'Walt Disney Imagineers, they're called, the experts who think of all these things.'

Mary turned to their mother, who was

hanging clothes in a walk-in closet.

'Can we go swimming?' Mary asked. 'The water's a beautiful greeny-blue-turquoise-aquamarine. To paint it, I'd use cobalt blue with a touch of Prussian blue and a little viridian.'

'Smarty-pants,' John commented. 'The water's *blue*.'

'We'll get settled and showered and changed,' Mrs Midas said soothingly. 'Don't worry. We'll do everything. We have two entire weeks. It's almost time for dinner now. We'll swim tomorrow.'

'Good idea!' said Mr Midas with a cheerful grin. 'I'm going to try the golf courses. I wonder which one's best – the Magnolia Golf Course, the Palm Golf Course, Osprey Ridge, Bonnet Creek or Eagle Pines? I'll have to play them all. And when you've done enough swimming there are a thousand rides.'

'I want to go to Spaceship Earth and Future World,' John said. He had been studying brochures and the Walt Disney World official map, with Mary peering over his shoulder.

'I'm curious about all the national pavilions in the Epcot Center,' Mrs Midas said. 'I've read there are all kinds of delicious foreign foods.'

'Journey into Imagination,' John said. 'World of Motion, Universe of Energy . . .'

'I'd like to see the Wonders of Life exhibition,' Mary said. 'What are the Wonders of Life, do you think?'

'Yes!' Mr Midas interrupted, so John did not have to attempt to answer her difficult question. 'See it all! Let's do it right. After I've worked a little on my golf.'

They spent so much time discussing the attractions shown on the map that dinner took a long time. In spite of all the talk

about their plans, though, Mary took good care to study the menu.

'I wonder what Florida Chocolate Cream Surprise is like,' she said. 'Or should I try the chocolate Mickey Mousse?'

'You get the surprise,' Mrs Midas suggested, 'and I'll get the mousse. Then we can share.'

Mary liked that idea. She liked it even more when her mother said she found the mousse a bit too sweet. Mary was able to finish both desserts.

'Gross!' John protested, wrinkling his nose.

'It's holiday time,' Mrs Midas pointed out in Mary's defence.

Mary happily licked her lips.

'Yum, yum,' was her only comment.

The more chocolate she had, the more she wanted.

It had been a long day and they were all tired.

Mary and John were sharing one of the bedrooms. Mary pretended to fall asleep as soon as she got into her bed. When she heard John's steady deep breathing and knew that he was really asleep, she slid her suitcase from its hiding-place under her bed, took the chocolate box from under her jeans, tiptoed with it to the bathroom, and locked herself in.

With eager fingers, she tore aside the

Cellophane wrapping and opened the box. There, nestling in a cushion of cotton-wool, lay a single, tiny, golden ball.

'Only one!' she muttered disappointedly.

Even though the box was a gift, she felt cheated. But, with a fingernail, she peeled off the gold foil to reveal a plain, dark ball of chocolate, and popped it into her mouth. The chocolate rapidly melted, leaving the most chocolatey chocolate taste she had ever tasted in her whole life.

She suddenly felt very sleepy.

Four

THE MOST CHOCOLATEY chocolate taste she had ever tasted . . .

When Mary awoke the following morning, the taste of chocolate was still strong and sweet in her mouth.

John got up first. He swished open the curtains and sunshine brightened the room.

'Another perfect day!' he announced.

'What's the time?' Mary mumbled.

'Time to get up! We're in the Magic Kingdom of Walt Disney World and this is Day One.'

'Are Mummy and Daddy up?'

'Last night they said you and I should go to the coffee shop and have breakfast on our own. Daddy said he's going to the Magnolia Golf Course and Mummy's going to have a lazy morning. We have our passes. We can do anything we like.'

'OK. Go ahead. I'll meet you in the coffee shop in a few minutes.'

She did not need to tell him twice.

John had almost finished digging into a broad slice of honeydew melon by the time Mary found him. His chin was glistening with juice.

'We ought to get Mickey Mouse T-shirts,' he said, 'and those black beanies with Mickey Mouse ears.' He was wearing his Zack Fink T-shirt. Zack was John's favourite rock star.

A waitress brought John a dish bearing a heap of pancakes and little sausages, and a silver jug of maple syrup.

'I'm going to see if there are any Minnie

Mouse T-shirts,' Mary said. 'Mickey is more famous, but Minnie is his girlfriend – his mouse-friend. She always has been.'

The waitress gave Mary a menu.

'It all looks so good,' she said. 'It's hard to choose.'

The waitress smiled sympathetically and said she'd be back. When she had gone, Mary looked around to make sure nobody else was listening, leaned forward over the table, and said in a low voice, 'Since when have we had chocolate toothpaste?'

John gave her a hard look.

'Did you say chocolate toothpaste?'

'Yes. Just now, when I brushed my teeth,

the toothpaste tasted like chocolate.'

John did not laugh. It sounded to him as though his sister had experienced an early symptom of the chocolate touch. He, himself, had had the chocolate touch last spring, though nobody believed him. That is one of the strangest features of the chocolate touch: it's an unbelievable condition which affects only a few people, when they become dangerously greedy for chocolate. It probably won't happen to you, but it could.

The chocolate touch is what is called 'progressive magic'. It starts simply: everything you eat and drink turns into chocolate. The magic becomes stronger: everything your lips touch turns into chocolate, and the chocolatisation spreads and spreads. For instance, when John's lips touched the mouthpiece of his trumpet, his whole trumpet turned into chocolate; and when he kissed his mother's cheek . . . Well, you can guess the result. As you can imagine, the chocolate touch soon causes mega-thirst and inconvenience.

After Dr Cranium, the Midases' family doctor, conducted a lot of tests, he said John had chocolatitis. He didn't know what to do about it. John had to find out for himself that greed is in the mind.

John told Mary all he knew about the chocolate touch. Like everyone else he had ever told, she didn't believe a word he said.

The waitress came back.

'Is the orange juice freshly squeezed?' Mary asked.

'It sure is, honey. You're in Florida, the Sunshine State.'

'Orange juice then, please. Muesli with low-fat milk. Soft-scrambled eggs and crispy bacon. Wholewheat toast and blueberry jam. And a glass of milk. Low-fat milk.'

The waitress soon returned with Mary's order.

Mary tilted the tall glass of orange juice against her lower lip and some of the ice-cold juice flowed into her mouth and down her throat. She raised her eyebrows high and her eyes bulged with astonishment.

'Chocolate-flavoured orange juice!' she exclaimed. 'That's really weird!'

'It'll get weirder,' John earnestly told her. 'Believe me, there's only one thing you can do. You . . .'

'Oh, hush! This must be a dream. Perhaps my cereal will taste of chocolate! This is fun!'

'It won't be fun for long,' John warned her. 'Listen . . .'

'Oh, pooh!'

Mary sampled the muesli, the bacon and eggs, the toast and the milk. Chocolate, chocolate, chocolate, chocolate, chocolate. As everything turned into chocolate in her mouth, she smiled.

'It's all quite realistic,' she admitted.

'That's because it's all real.'

'Oh, John! I know I'm dreaming, so none of this matters.'

'I'm not dreaming,' he argued.

'Of course not. I'm doing the dreaming. You're only someone in my dream. If what you told me was true, why doesn't anyone remember any of it? Huh?'

'I've often tried to work that out. I suppose that's part of the magic. Things go back to where they were. Do you want me to prove you're awake?'

Mary laughed. 'You're making my head spin. Yes, go ahead.'

John reached out and gently pinched the

bare upper part of her left arm.

'Well, that wasn't much,' she said.

John pinched her again, much harder.

'Ouch! Hey, that hurt!'

'Do you think you dreamed it?'

'Certainly.' She rubbed her arm. The pain faded. 'And now I'd like to dream you get lost. You and your silly stories . . .'

Sometimes, Mary could be very stubborn.

Five

MARY AND JOHN had learned that
when they were beginning to quarrel
the smart thing to do was to give each other
a break, so that they could both cool off.
There was plenty of space to do that.

She went to Fantasyland. He went to
Frontierland.

They found so much to see that the
morning passed quickly, though each of
them thought that things would have been
more interesting if they had been together,
comparing opinions. Like most other
brothers and sisters, they had their ups and
downs. There were occasional arguments,
but they were fond of each other.

Why did John say such stupid things in

my dream? Mary asked herself, while John wondered how long it would take Mary to get real and face up to what was happening.

They could not both be right.

In their separate parts of the Magic Kingdom, at lunch-time, they began to feel hungry.

John found a café where he ordered a double cheeseburger with French fries and a Coke. At the same time, on the opposite side of the park, Mary got herself a foot-long hot dog to go. Usually, she would have chosen a chocolate milk-shake to wash it down, but she felt extra-thirsty, so she got a giant lemonade with lots of crushed ice.

She sat on a bench beside a hedge of pink hibiscus, in the shade of a palm-tree, and looked forward to her private picnic. She could get along without the company of her brother.

'The trouble with John,' she complained, 'is he's so immature.'

'Did you say something to me, little girl?' asked an elderly lady who happened to be passing by with her young grandson.

'Oh, no, excuse me!' Mary replied, blushing with embarrassment. 'I was just thinking aloud.'

'That's perfectly all right,' the lady said, peeping down kindly over her spectacles. 'We all do that sometimes.'

When they had walked past, the boy turned and grinned and stuck out his tongue. Mary wished she had something to throw at him.

But then she concentrated on enjoying the first bite of her hot dog. Any other day, it would have made her mouth water. Today, however, inside her mouth there was only a sticky trickle that tasted of chocolate.

Munch!

The toasted soft bun, the sauerkraut, the mustard and the firm-then-squishy hot dog all tasted the same – of chocolate.

And then Mary saw with a shock of dismay that the magic of the chocolate touch, as John had predicted, was strengthening. As she watched, the hot dog turned to chocolate. Everything in it was totally chocolatified.

She gazed at the ice-cold giant lemonade with thirsty yearning but little hope. When she brought the edge of the plastic tumbler against her lower lip, the change was even faster than she had feared. Immediately, she found she was holding a chocolate tumbler of chocolateade and chocolate ice.

Would she be able to live on an all-chocolate diet? She doubted it. The thought was sickening and frightening. She was worried.

I'd better go back to the hotel, she thought. Mummy will know what to do.

But when Mary called their suite from a telephone in the hotel lobby there was no reply. She asked the desk clerk for the key.

'Mary Midas?' the clerk said. 'There's a message for you.'

Mary read it as she waited for the lift.

Mary, sweetheart,
I hope you and John had a great
time exploring. Daddy's trying the
Palm Golf Course and I'm going
for a walk. Get yourselves some
nice sandwiches and drinks in the
coffee shop. Then why don't you
two have a refreshing swim? The

clerk says there's a 'real cute'
lifeguard. Daddy and I will be
back soon and we'll all do
something together.

Love and xxx
Mummy

Mary's new pale-blue swimsuit and a towel were laid out on her bed. John's new green swimming shorts and a towel were laid out on his. There was no sign of John, so Mary wrote a note for him and left it with the key at the front desk.

John,
Gone swimming.

Mary

Six

THE BIG MICKEY Mouse swimming-pool glittered blue and silver in brilliant sunshine from the cloudless blue sky. The pool was surrounded by a circular stone terrace within a circle of flower-beds and tall palm-trees.

While many people enjoyed diving, splashing, swimming and floating in the water, others relaxed on lounge chairs, watching, chatting, sipping drinks, reading or simply lying back and improving their tans.

A perfect place for a holiday! Mary thought.

She climbed the three steps to the diving-board.

Mary was a good swimmer. She had school diplomas saying she could swim the breast-stroke, the crawl and the back-stroke. She could also dive – no fancy somersaults or twists off high boards, but ordinary, straight dives. She was confident but self-conscious as she walked slowly along the springy board, and then she stood still, with her arms outstretched and her toes curled over the edge, considering jumping off, thinking about it, planning it.

When you stand on a diving-board, about to dive, you can't help imagining that everybody in and around the pool is staring at you. She wanted to make sure that she entered the water neatly, a credit to her school, her family and herself. For a few moments she was able to forget the chocolate touch.

She did some small bouncing jumps; one, two, three, and then, with a determined

effort, she sprang up as high as she could –
up, out, over and down.

The dive was one of her best. There was
only a slight splash. Her hands, firmly
pressed together, her rigid arms and her
bowed head smoothly slid into the cool,
clear water.

But then something shocking happened.
As soon as her lips went below the surface,
there was a transformation. All the water in
the pool instantly turned into liquid
chocolate.

Mary floated up with chocolate-water

streaming from her hair. She blinked
chocolate from her eyes and saw an
amazing scene. All over the pool, men,
women and children were snorting,
spluttering and spitting chocolate. The
dark-brown fluid was churned into a pale-
brown froth as panicky swimmers thrashed
their ways to the sides of the pool and
clambered up ladders to get out.

'Ugh!'

'Ee-yuck!'

'Phooey!'

The lifeguard was
heroically active,
pulling people out
of the chocolate
pool.

When he offered
one small boy a
hand, however, he didn't grab it.

'Hold on!' the lifeguard shouted. 'Don't

be afraid! I'll help you!'

'Who's afraid?' the boy answered. 'I like it here. It's chocolate.'

But he was an exception. As Mary knew by now, too much chocolate can make you feel sick.

One woman screamed, or tried to scream, but the sound came out as a chocolatey gurgle.

'It's all horrible and brown and icky!' a girl protested. 'My lovely pink swimsuit's ruined!'

'What's going on here?' a man angrily demanded. 'Who's responsible for this?'

Mary was so embarrassed and frightened, she ran away.

She didn't know what might happen under a shower, so she just towelled herself dry, pulled on her T-shirt and jeans and sandals, and kept going.

Seven

MARY HURRIEDLY STUMBLED away from the hotel, past Mickey's Starland, past the Magic Kingdom's legendary castle, with its towering ramparts, turrets, steeples and high-flying flags, around the central crossroads plaza, and down along Main Street, USA.

Shaken, confused and very, very thirsty, she slumped miserably on a bench and burst into tears. Of all the visitors strolling contentedly to and fro along the pavements, nobody could possibly know it was her fault the pool had turned into liquid chocolate and that she had spoiled the afternoon for all those swimmers. But Mary knew. She felt awful. She dreaded telling her parents.

If she didn't tell them,
would they find out?

When the young men and women on the staff of Walt Disney World smile and say, 'Have a nice day!' they really expect you to have one. Tears are unusual in that magical place. But there was Mary, a conspicuous oddity, sitting bent forward, her elbows on her knees and her face in her hands, with sobs shaking her shoulders and tears pouring down her cheeks.

She had been there for only a few minutes, wondering what she should do, when she heard happy music approaching. It was three o'clock, time for the daily parade.

Mickey Mouse and his special, closest friends, Minnie Mouse, Donald Duck, Pluto and Goofy, were standing on an open float, rocking in time with the music and waving to all their cheering admirers.

Looking at Mickey and Minnie that fine afternoon, you would have found it almost impossible to realise that they are more than sixty years of age, with their shiny, little, round noses, radiant smiles, and not the slightest touch of grey in their black hair. Their lively yet dignified manner gave an impression of them being the healthy, wealthy, wise, happy, young Prince and Princess of Mice.

As always, their costumes were elegant. Mickey was wearing his favourite yellow bow tie, a white shirt and waistcoat, red trousers with two large white buttons in front, a black tailcoat, white gloves and well-polished black shoes. Minnie was wearing a short-sleeved, low-neck, red dress with large white spots and a matching red and white bow in her hair, white gloves like Mickey's and red, high-heeled shoes. Being a well brought up mouse, she had applied just the right amount of make-up – only a little lipstick, a hint of pink on her cheeks, and sufficient blue on her eyelids to emphasise her long, curling, black lashes and the brightness of her big eyes. They were a romantic couple.

Mary, in normal circumstances, would have liked nothing better than a chance to see them live, up close; but never had her circumstances been less normal.

As the float came near to where Mary sat, Minnie nudged Mickey and spoke urgently into his ear.

'Look at that poor girl!' she said. 'What can be wrong?'

Mickey was a quick decision-maker.

'Stop the float!' he ordered, in a voice that made the driver stamp on the brakes.

In spite of being the most famous and respected mice in the whole world, Mickey and Minnie were still able to feel sympathetic affection for ordinary folk, especially when any of them seemed in trouble.

'Hello, little girl!' Mickey said in a reassuringly cheerful manner, placing a hand on Mary's shoulder.

'Please don't cry,' Minnie said, patting Mary's other shoulder. 'Not in the Magic Kingdom!'

Mary tried hard to stop crying, but the tears kept flowing.

'Give me your handkerchief,' Minnie said to Mickey, who immediately passed her a large white one from his pocket.

'There, there,' Minnie said, gently

dabbing Mary's eyes. 'Have a good blow. It'll make you feel better. That's what I do.'

Minnie held the handkerchief so that Mary could blow her nose.

Mary did so. She pulled herself together. She sat up straight. The tears stopped. She even managed a small, grateful smile.

'I'm sorry,' she whispered.

'What's your name?' Minnie asked.

'Mary. Mary Midas.'

'That's a nice name,' Minnie said.

'What's bothering you?' Mickey kindly enquired. Although he was an international star of motion pictures, television and comic books, he had always remained a decent, down-to-earth, practical mouse. 'There must be something we can do to help.'

As always happened when Mickey and Minnie walked among the public, a group of eager, curious fans was forming around the two celebrities. The group was rapidly becoming a crowd. There were many cameras and some camcorders. Mickey and Minnie were accustomed to such attention, but it made Mary feel shy.

'I'm afraid you'll think I'm very silly,' Mary slowly began.

'Of course we won't, dear,' Minnie encouragingly assured her.

'Well,' Mary said, looking from Minnie to Mickey. 'A terrible thing happened. I didn't mean to do it.'

'You can tell us anything,' Mickey said.

'I turned the water in the pool at the hotel . . . into chocolate.'

Mickey and Minnie looked at each other. She gave him a little frown, to tell him that he shouldn't laugh at Mary, but he found it impossible not to. He couldn't believe that she really meant exactly what she said.

'I've heard some funny stories in my time,' he said, 'but that one deserves some sort of prize!'

Mickey put his arm round Mary's back and gave her a friendly Uncle Mickey sort of hug – and a quick kiss.

It all happened suddenly.

Somehow, Mary's lips brushed against his cheek.

Mickey Mouse instantly turned into a chocolate statue.

Eight

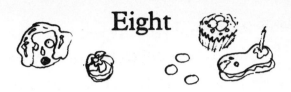

A SHORT TIME later that afternoon, the President of the United States was sitting in the Oval Office of the White House. Washington is always a busy place for most of the people there most of the time, but sometimes the President is able to take a little time off to sit quietly by himself. On this occasion, he was resting in a comfortable armchair away from his desk, watching a soap opera on television.

It was not very exciting and he was almost asleep, when a news presenter came on.

'We interrupt this programme to bring you a news bulletin,' he announced. 'Mickey Mouse is seriously ill.'

The President was shocked wide awake.

'First reports from Walt Disney World in Florida are unclear as to the exact nature of Mickey's condition,' the presenter went on. 'A Magic Kingdom spokesman said Mickey has been taken to a first-aid station and is in the best of medical care. He appeared to be in his usual good spirits as he led his traditional afternoon parade along Main Street, USA. He stopped to greet a well-wisher at the roadside at six minutes after three, suffered a massive attack of some kind and was unable to move or speak. Here's the latest from our man on the spot. Harry? What's the situation as of now?'

'Well, Bob,' said a worried-looking reporter, standing where the incident had occurred. Behind him stood a crowd of spectators, some of them waving at the camera. 'Nobody here is making much sense right now. The tragedy has made witnesses numb with grief. One of them typically was only able to say that Mickey was perfectly OK one minute, and the next minute he suddenly turned brown.'

'Did you say brown, Harry?' the presenter interrupted. 'Can we have some details on that?'

'Doctors here promise to make a statement when they have completed their examination,' Harry said. 'In the meantime, though, I have some tape from a tourist's camcorder.'

The President got out of his chair and moved close to the television set.

There was a series of jerky shots of the parade and of Mickey and Minnie leaving the float and standing by a girl who was weeping. Mickey and Minnie spoke with her. Then Mickey hugged the girl and kissed her cheek – and turned brown. Minnie approached the camera and held up a white-gloved hand until it filled the screen.

'That's all we have,' Harry said when he was back in the television picture. 'The lady who made the video said Minnie did not want Mickey filmed or photographed in his present state. She was gracious but firm. "Mickey isn't himself," she explained.'

The President hurried over to his desk and picked up a telephone.

'Get the Vice President and the Director of the FBI and my press secretary in here right away,' he said. 'And my personal doctor. We have a national emergency on our hands.'

Soon the Oval Office was full of the President's senior advisers and their assistants and secretaries, and there was a lot of anxious and excited talk.

There were many urgent telephone calls to and from the office. One of the callers was the Governor of Florida, who happened to be enjoying a holiday in Walt Disney World at the time.

'I've just been in conference with Minnie Mouse,' the Governor told the President. 'She deserves a lot of credit. She's brave. She's awful upset though, and she's saying some strange things. She says Mickey is totally paralysed on account of the fact he's chocolate.'

The President does his best to be polite to public officials at times of crisis, even when they talk nonsense. However, for a moment, he lost his temper.

'*Are you crazy*?' he demanded. 'This is no time for jokes. Millions of voters love Mickey Mouse. I do myself . . .'

'Me too, Mr President.'

'I want a serious report of what's going on.'

'I know it's hard to believe, Mr President, but that's what she said. I don't doubt her sincerity. She said they have to keep Mickey out of the sun or he might melt. And she said some kid said it was her fault – the little girl she and Mickey were comforting.'

'What's the child's name?' the President asked.

'Mary. Mary Midas.'

'I want to speak with her.'

'But she's a weird, nervous kid. She said she turned a whole swimming-pool into chocolate! I got her out of here. She's been sent back to her hotel. Maybe her parents can calm her down.'

'You idiot!'

'Mr President!'

'I'm sorry. But we need all the information we can get. Please bring Minnie to the phone.'

'Yes, Mr President.'

After a brief conversation with the grieving Minnie, in which the President expressed his own heartfelt, personal sympathy, pledged the nation's support, and asked her some questions, he hung up the telephone and turned to his closest, most trusted aide.

'Here's what we have to do . . .'

Nine

BACK AT THE hotel, Mary tried to explain to her mother and father why she had fled from the pool and what she had accidentally done to Mickey Mouse.

'Hold it, Mary!' Mr Midas said with a puzzled expression on his face, part smile, part frown. 'There's no need for these fantastic excuses. If the water in the swimming-pool changed colour, there has to be a logical explanation. Sometimes there is temporary pollution in even the best-run water supplies. It isn't the hotel's fault, and it certainly isn't your fault. No doubt they'll clean the pool and they'll soon be able to refill it with pure water. As for Mickey Mouse . . . I'm sure he works

very hard, entertaining you kids. He must
be overtired. He probably got too much
sun and fainted.'

'It's the chocolate touch,' Mary insisted.
'My lips touched him and he turned to
chocolate. You believe me, don't you,
John?'

'Enough!' Mr Midas said impatiently.

'Really, both of you!' Mrs Midas
protested. 'We were worried about you,
Mary, and now you're back, so everything's

fine. But I can see the pool made a mess of your hair. Why don't you wash it? You can use my shampoo. The bathroom water is all right. Put on a nice dress. And, John – you could use a wash and a brush. We'll do some sightseeing. There's so much to see. And then we'll have an early meal.'

'Right!' Mr Midas agreed enthusiastically. 'Let's get going!'

While Mary was wondering how she could have a shower without letting any water touch her lips, the doorbell rang.

Mrs Midas opened the door.

Two men were standing there. They looked like twins – both tall, broad-shouldered, smooth-shaven and dressed in black suits.

'Mrs Midas?' one of them asked.

'Yes. What is it?'

'Secret Service, ma'am,' the second one said politely, showing a gold badge. 'Is Mary Midas here?'

'Yes. Is something wrong?'

'May we come in?' asked Agent Number One.

Mrs Midas opened the door wider and moved aside, and they came in.

'What's going on here?' asked Mr Midas.

'We have received instructions for the

Midas family,' said Agent Number Two.

'You are to arrive at Orlando International Airport tomorrow morning at zero eight forty-five hours. That's a quarter of nine.'

'With all your baggage, prepared for nine o'clock take-off,' said Agent Number One.

'A limousine will be provided.'

'There will be an escort.'

'Until then, you will remain in the hotel.'

'In your suite.'

'You will make no telephone calls.'

'Your telephone is disconnected, as of now.'

'A room-service waiter will take your food orders.'

'He is one of our men.'

'Who says?' Mr Midas indignantly demanded.

Agent Number Two permitted himself to smile.

'The President of the United States says.'

Ten

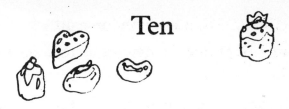

'ANYWAY,' MRS MIDAS said con-
solingly, as the white stretch-limo
smoothly rushed them along the Beeline
Expressway the next morning, 'they're
treating us like VIPs.'

'What are VIPs?' Mary asked.

'Very Important Persons,' John said.

'In this case,' grumbled Mr Midas, 'more
like Very Important Prisoners.'

Everyone was treating them with the
greatest courtesy – but telling them
nothing. One reason was that their escorts
knew no more than they did about the
purpose of their urgent journey.

At the airport, the limousine took them
straight to the place where a gleaming,

silver and white, four-engined plane was waiting. It was an impressive sight, with UNITED STATES OF AMERICA in big letters on its side. The President had sent Air Force One, his own official, long-distance plane, to collect Mary and her family.

The plane's interior was luxurious. The Midases were shown into a compartment furnished like a living-room, with a thick, soft carpet and plenty of space between comfortable armchairs. In happier, less mysterious circumstances, Mary would have been able to enjoy the experience. As things were, she felt hungry, thirsty and afraid.

When the plane was high enough, a smartly uniformed steward said they could unfasten their seat belts and asked whether they wished to see the breakfast menu.

'We've had breakfast,' Mr Midas said.

'At least, three of us have,' said Mrs Midas. 'Mary doesn't feel very well.'

'I'm sorry to hear that,' the steward said. He gave her a little pat on the head, which she hated. 'Perhaps some light refreshments? Coffee? Champagne? Soft drinks for the children?'

'What I wish,' Mr Midas said, 'is for someone to tell me where this plane is taking us and why, if that isn't too much to ask.'

'The destination is Andrew's, sir. Andrew's Air Force Base. We have not been briefed as to why.'

'And where is that?'

'Washington, sir.'

Mr and Mrs Midas had coffee. John had a Coke. Mary pretended she wasn't thirsty. The thought of drinking something that would turn into chocolate made her feel quite sick. Enviously watching the others enjoy their drinks, Mary had nothing.

John murmured sympathetically and tried not to let her see how much he was enjoying his drink.

At Andrew's Air Force Base, an Air Force major escorted the Midas family to a helicopter.

After a short flight, the helicopter hovered briefly and slowly descended and landed on the lawn in front of the White House.

A Marine lieutenant took the Midases to the building, where a civilian with grey hair and a red face bustled them along corridors, across a hall, past a desk and through doors.

Mary's parents and brother were kept in a waiting-room while Mary was taken into the White House clinic, a miniature private hospital, which is fully equipped to deal with any medical problem.

Several distinguished doctors had been brought there to examine her. They had come from the Bethesda Naval Hospital, the Johns Hopkins Hospital in Baltimore and New York's Mount Sinai Hospital.

One by one, the specialists gave Mary a thorough going-over. Now and then they discussed her in low voices that she could not make out.

At last, the doctor who seemed to be the head of the team spoke to her. 'All right, little lady. You can get dressed now.'

That was all.

The President was friendly.

In the Oval Office, he shook Mr and Mrs

Midas by the hand. He even shook the
hands of John and Mary.

He introduced them to some of his staff
and advisers.

'I appreciate your coming here, Mary,'
the President said.

'We didn't have any choice, Mr
President,' her father said.

'Nor did I,' said the President. 'We must
act fast. Mickey Mouse has a medical
problem. He's in quarantine. Nobody will

be allowed to visit him until it's cleared up. Some of the country's top medical men are working on it. Right now we have to send a clear message to the American people that there is no cause for alarm. There has been some irresponsible talk. There are wild rumours that Mickey has some kind of fatal new disease and there's danger of an epidemic. There's a report – unconfirmed, of course (the media are way out of line on this one) – that Mickey Mouse has turned into . . . no, I'm not going to repeat it.'

The President gave Mary a big smile. 'Mary,' he said, 'since some pictures have gone out, you're right in the middle of this. We have to assure the people of this country – the people of the world – that you did not cause Mickey to suffer his present health difficulty. We must not allow our natural concern for Mickey to become a national panic. The very dollar might collapse. The doctors have notified me they have found no sign that you are carrying any infection. Now you and I must prove that for all the world to see.'

What could she do? Mary wondered. But she was already being hustled from the Oval Office, and Mr and Mrs Midas and John could only anxiously follow.

Mary found herself with the President in the middle of a small stage in the auditorium used for press conferences. First there was to be a photo opportunity. There was a crowd of television crews and stills photographers. About a hundred cameras of all sizes were pointing at the stage. The lights were bright and hot.

'If you people are ready?' the President said, looking as relaxed and confident as he always did on such occasions. 'Now, Mary. It has been said that the touch of your lips had a certain harmful effect on our dear friend Mickey Mouse. Of course, medical experts agree that there's no way you could have harmed him. So what I want you to do for the photographers is simply this. I want you to give me a big kiss on my cheek. OK?'

'Oh, no, Mr President. I can't do that!'

The President winked at the photographers then turned to Mary and leaned down so that his face was within her reach. Good-naturedly chuckling, he said, 'It's all right, Mary. My wife won't mind. Go ahead, give me a kiss.'

'Please, Mr President! Really, I mustn't.'

The President's smile faded. 'You must, Mary. You can't refuse. This is the President speaking. I'm giving you a Presidential order.'

'Go on, Mary,' said Mr Midas.

With extreme reluctance, Mary lightly kissed the President's cheek.

Instantaneously, the President of the United States turned into a statue of chocolate.

Eleven

THERE WAS SUCH an uproar, such chaos, in the President's press-conference room that the Midas family were able to slip away. Nobody attempted to stop them from leaving the White House. After all, there is no law against turning the President into chocolate. It had never happened before, and probably won't ever happen again.

Mary felt almost as bad about the President as she felt about Mickey Mouse – and herself. She could not imagine how she would be able to survive the chocolate touch.

'It's all right, Mummy,' she said doubtfully. 'This is only a dream I'm dreaming.' She sounded more optimistic than she felt.

A taxi. A train. Another taxi. And they were back home in a calm, leafy suburb of New York.

Mr and Mrs Midas went into their bedroom, to talk about the situation without frightening their daughter. They did not know what to do.

Mary and John were alone together in the kitchen. John was drinking a glass of cold milk. Mary was just sitting there, feeling miserable.

'It's bad,' John acknowledged. 'I know how you feel.'

'If only I hadn't eaten that chocolate. I'm sure it was magic.'

'What chocolate?' John asked.

'I didn't want you to know about it. I didn't want to share it with you. I've been such a pig. John, I'm sorry.'

'It's all right. I understand. That's not the sort of chocolate that anyone ever shares. Where did you get it?'

Mary told her brother about the old man in the supermarket, the strange coin he had given her, and the giant chocolate box he had said she could buy with it.

John asked her to describe the old man. She did. 'That's him!' John exclaimed. 'He's the one who gave me the chocolate touch! You'll have to go and find him. It's the only way. Go back to the supermarket – right now.'

'Is that how to end the dream?' Mary asked.

'I already told you: it isn't a dream. I tried to prove it. Do you want another pinch?'

'No. That really hurt. But . . . '

'Please, Mary. Please go. It's the only hope. You're sometimes a pain in the neck, but you are my little sister. I don't want to seem mushy, but, I must admit, I love you very much.'

'You do?!'

Without thinking, Mary grabbed John and gave him a big kiss.

Twelve

PEDALLING HER BICYCLE as fast as she could, Mary took only a few breathless minutes to reach the mall.

She pushed past two old ladies and almost bumped into the slowly sliding automatic glass doors in her hurry to get into the supermarket.

There was the old man, sitting beside a cash register at the end of the checkout counters. He was finishing a conversation with an extraordinarily large boy when Mary approached.

'Very well,' the old man was saying to him. 'If you're absolutely sure. My special chocolate boxes are on display away back in the far corner on the left.'

Without saying a word of thanks, the boy
eagerly waddled away.

'Well, well, well,' the old man said.
'Mary Midas! How nice to see you. I
suppose you've been getting all the
chocolate you desired?'

'Much, much more!' Mary said in a
hoarse voice of despair. She blurted out an
account of all the horrors of the past day
and a half – the pool, Mickey Mouse, the
President and . . .

'And worst of all,' she cried, 'my very own
dear brother! A lifeless lump of chocolate!

You've got to do something!'

'Did you say *I've* got to do something?'

He gazed reproachfully over the top of his glasses, scratched the white hair at the crown of his head, and thoughtfully brushed his white moustache with the back of a forefinger.

'If you turned them into chocolate, can't you turn them back again?' Mary asked.

'*I* didn't turn anything or anyone into chocolate,' the old man mildly pointed out.

Mary's face reddened with shame.

'No,' she confessed. 'You're right. I did. It has all been my doing. I know I've been horribly piggish. I'd rather *die* than let John stay chocolate.'

'I don't think there's any need for you to die to put things right. Perhaps you can suggest something a bit less drastic?'

'If you'd undo all the bad things I've done ... I'd ... you could turn me into a pig if you like.'

'No, Mary, I wouldn't like that. You've had quite enough piggishness. If you really want things to be as they were . . .'

'Oh, yes, I do! I do!'

'. . . and if you're going to be your true, pleasant, unselfish self . . .'

'I am, I am, I promise!'

'. . . then I don't see any further problem,' the old man said. 'Time is a magical element, you know. Magic is really quite useful. Magic can do things, and it can undo things. Magic can even make time twist and turn back. To turn time back without magic would be difficult. You'd have to stop the world from turning in its usual way, and then you would have to turn it backwards – one complete turn for every day. That would cause certain difficulties. For example, every loose thing on our planet would fall off and everybody, every living creature, would be killed. Fortunately, magic can turn back the clock and the calendar without losing a single pebble or an ant. So, Mary, as magicians used to say, hey, presto! As far as I'm concerned, case closed; as far as you're concerned, all is well. You may kiss me, if you wish.'

Mary hesitated.

'Perfectly safe now,' he promised.

Mary kissed the old man's pink cheek, which smelled faintly of lavender soap.

When she saw that he remained a cheerful, lively, pink-and-white old man, she was overjoyed.

'Oh, there you are, my girl!' Mrs Midas said. 'Please don't go out again. We have things to do to get ready. You'd better pack. And would you help John with his packing? You know what an awful muddle he makes of his clothes.'

'Gladly, Mummy!' Mary exclaimed. It really was the day before yesterday again.

Mrs Midas smiled to see Mary looking so happy about their trip. Helping John pack had never before been Mary's idea of fun.

'And don't get him worked up any more than he is already,' Mrs Midas said. 'I want you both to get a good night's sleep. Tomorrow's the big day, the first day of our holiday. Florida, here we come!'

Mary was just about to ask her mother whether she had heard anything about the health of the President and Mickey Mouse, but at that moment John came bounding into the room with a big grin on his face, and she knew for sure that everything was all right.

So it was a dream, Mary thought. Or was it? She thoughtfully felt the upper part of her left arm. Apparently the old man had undone all the events that had caused such grief but one. He had caused her to keep the result of John's pinching as a little souvenir, a reminder.

The next day, when they flew down to Orlando, the bruise on her arm was still there, and she was grateful. Now John and she both knew the secret of the chocolate touch.

If you enjoyed this
MAMMOTH READ try:

How's Harry?

By *Steve May*
Illustrated by *Philip Hopman*

Harry's a hamster and Kate's going to
have him for a pet, whatever her parents
say. Her dad doesn't think she can look
after him properly – every five minutes
he asks, 'How's Harry?'

It drives Kate mad. All she wants
is to help Harry find happiness. But
when she asks Harry what he wants
from life, he can't tell her.

Kate decides she knows best.
She will take Harry back to his
roots . . . in the Syrian desert!

I LOVE
HARRY

Are you his ultimate fan?

Written by Jim Maloney

Edited by Jen Wainwright and Nicola Baxter
Design by Barbara Ward
Cover design by Zoe Bradley

Picture Acknowledgements:
Front cover: Stuart Wilson/Getty Images
Back cover: KeystoneUSA-ZUMA/Rex Features

Picture section:
Page 1, Stephen Lovekin/Getty Images
Page 2, Steve Granitz/WireImage/Getty Images
Page 3, Al Pereira/WireImage/Getty Images
Page 4, Juan Naharro Gimenez/WireImage/Getty Images
Page 5, Brian Rasic/Rex Features
Pages 6–7, Venturelli/Getty Images
Page 8, Startraks Photo/Rex Features

First published in Great Britain in 2013 by Buster Books,
an imprint of Michael O'Mara Books Limited, 9 Lion Yard, Tremadoc Road,
London SW4 7NQ

www.busterbooks.co.uk

Text copyright © Buster Books 2013

Artwork adapted from www.shutterstock.com

A CIP catalogue record for this book is available from the British Library.

ISBN: 978-1-78055-213-2

PLEASE NOTE: This book is not affiliated with or endorsed by One Direction or
any of their publishers or licensees.

10 9 8 7 6 5 4 3 2

Printed and bound in February 2013 by CPI Group (UK) Ltd, 108 Beddington Lane,
Croydon, CR0 4YY, United Kingdom.

Papers used by Buster Books are natural, recyclable products made from wood
grown in sustainable forests. The manufacturing processes conform to the
environmental regulations of the country of origin.